Content

The Potato Farm

Written by Sally Dunbier • Photographed by Wendy Ford

Our Uncle Dan has a potato farm.
It's fun to stay with him.

In spring, Uncle Dan plants the potatoes. He lets us help him. First we pick a potato that has sprouted.

Sprouts

Potato

Then we plant the potato in the soil and cover it up.

3

After about three weeks,
the shoots pop through the soil.
We help Uncle Dan pile more soil
around the shoots.

We put eggshells
around the potato plants
to keep the snails
and slugs away.

Sid the scarecrow
keeps the birds away.
They like the young shoots, too.

Did You Know?

Snails and slugs
will not crawl over
crushed eggshells.

5

After about eight weeks,
the potatoes are ready to go.
Each plant has lots of potatoes.
We help carry the potatoes
to the packing shed.

6

Did You Know?

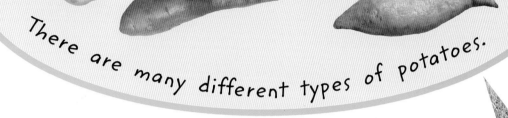

There are many different types of potatoes.

Sometimes, after the potatoes are dug, we have a potato picnic.
We wash the potatoes and chop them into pieces.
Uncle Dan cooks the potatoes in the oven.

New potatoes are delicious!

Grow a Bean Sprout Name

You will need:

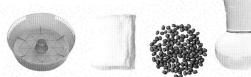

1. Put cotton wool in the dish. Sprinkle water over it.

2. Write your name using the mung beans.

3. Put the bowl in the sun. Keep the wool wet.

Beans, Beans, Beans

Baked beans,
butter beans,
big fat lima beans,
long thin string beans –
those are just a few.

Fried

Mashed

Which way do you like potatoes cooked?

Boiled

Baked

Crisp

9

Gobble Up Your Greens

Pinto beans

Red kidney beans

Soy beans

Green peas

Black-eyed peas

Split peas

Green beans,
black beans,
big fat kidney beans,
red hot chilli beans,
jumping beans, too.
Pea beans,
pinto beans,
don't forget soya beans.
Last of all, best of all,
I like jelly beans!

Lucia and James L. Hymes, Jr.

People can make many delicious meals using peas and beans.

13

Farms Around the World

On farms all around the world, people grow crops or raise animals. The kind of farming they do often depends on the place in which they live.

People grow fruit in many parts of the world. Peaches grow best in places that are not too hot and not too cold.

Cotton farms are found in warm places. Cotton is made into cloth.

Wheat farms are found in dry, mild places. Wheat is used in many cereals.

Some people even grow flowers on farms. They sell the bulbs and flowers all around the world.

People raise animals such as sheep on farms, too. Sheep are shorn for their wool. Sheep farmers often use dogs to help them with their work.

18

People raise cattle
on farms, too.
Cattle are used for
their meat and their
milk. Cattle farmers
often use horses
to help them
with their work.

19

Barn Dance

Written by Avelyn Davidson • Illustrated by John Bennett

Bow to your partner,
stamp your feet.
Everybody dance
to the barnyard beat.

Twirl your partner,
around and around.
Clap your hooves
and paw the ground.

Baa with the sheep.
Moo with the cow.
Twirl your partner.
Give a bow.

22

Baa-baa, moo-moo,
cock-a-doodle doo!
Everybody promenade
two by two.

23

Around and around
the ring we go.
Cows to the centre,
do-si-do.

Spin with the turkey.
Trot with the horse.
The dance is done,
so bow, of course!

Bike Boy

A True Story

Written by Bill Keir
Photographed by Andy Belcher

Eli is eight and he lives on a farm.
When he is not at school,
Eli helps look after the goats.
Eli uses his farm bike
to help round up the goats.

27

One day after school,
Eli was counting the goats
and their kids, and he saw
that a kid was missing.
He told his mother.

"You'd better look for it,"
she said.

Eli jumped on his bike
and rode to the top of the hill.
From there, he could see
the whole farm.

Eli looked around,
but there was no sign
of the missing kid.

Then Eli saw a hawk.
"Maybe the hawk has seen
the lost kid," he thought to himself.
"I must hurry."

Eli raced across the fields.
He bounced over bumps
and splashed through the mud.

He nearly fell off his bike!

Suddenly, the engine stopped.

"Oh no!" thought Eli.
"I must get to the kid
before the hawk does."

Eli looked at the spark plug.

It was wet with mud.

Eli dried the spark plug with a rag.

Then he kicked the starter

and away he went!

The sun was going down.
"I must find the lost kid fast,"
thought Eli. "Where can it be?"

Then he saw the kid.
"Maaa, maaa," cried the kid.
Eli looked up.
The hawk was above him.
It had seen the kid, too.

Slowly, Eli crept towards
the kid. "Come on, little one," he said.
"I'll take you back to your mother."

But the kid was scared.
It began to run away. Eli ran, too.
"Got you!" he said.
He patted the kid's head.
"Let's go home," he said.

Soon the baby goat
was back with its mother,
having a drink of milk.

Eli counted the goats once more.
Yes, they were all there.

He rode his bike back to the house.
He washed the mud off his bike.
He put the bike away in the shed.

The bike needed a rest
after the day's hard work.
And so did Eli!

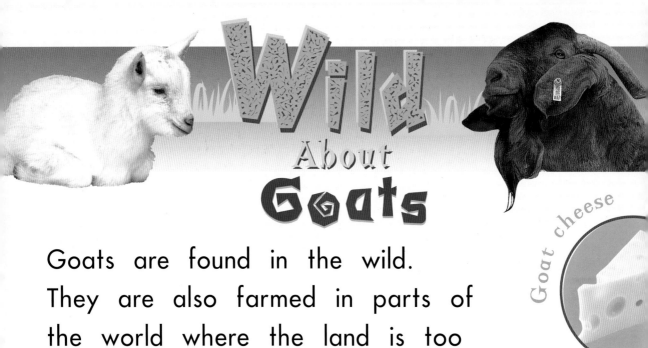

Wild About Goats

Goats are found in the wild. They are also farmed in parts of the world where the land is too steep and dry for sheep and cows.

Goat cheese

Goat milk

Nanny goat

Kid

Billy goat

39

The Goat Well

A Traditional African Folk Tale

Illustrated by Kiangyi Mo and Jingwen Wang

Once there was a boy
who saw a well in the desert.
When he looked in the well,
he saw no water,
but he saw a goat.
A goat had fallen into the well.

The boy saw a man
coming with two camels.
"Maybe I can play a trick
on this man," he said.

When the man was near the well,
the boy pulled out the goat.
"What is this?" said the man.

"This is my goat well,"
the boy said. "I pull out
a new goat each day."

"I would like a goat well,"
said the man. "I'll swap you my
camels for your goat well, but,
before you go, tell me your name."

"My name is Where-I-Can-Dance,"
said the boy, and away he went.

The next day, the man looked
in the well, but there was no goat.
All day, he stayed at the well,
but still there was no goat.
Then the man knew that
he had been tricked.

"I must find that boy," he said.
So he went to look for the boy
named Where-I-Can-Dance.

Soon the man came to a village. He asked a girl, "Do you know Where-I-Can-Dance?"

"You can dance here," she said.

"No, no," he said. "I am asking if you know Where-I-Can-Dance."

Again the girl said, "You can dance here."

The man was angry. "Take me to the Wise Woman of the village," he said. "Maybe she will know Where-I-Can-Dance."

But the Wise Woman only smiled. "You were tricked," she said. "You were tricked with a goat well, and tricked with a name."

The Wise Woman told the girl,
"A new boy with two camels is
in our village. Tell him that someone
named What-I-Must-Do wants him."

The boy came at once.
He asked, "Do you know
What-I-Must-Do?"

"Yes, I know what you must do,"
she said. "You must give back
the camels."

When the boy saw the man,
he knew he had been tricked
with the very trick he played.

"Oh, Wise Woman," said the boy, "you
tricked me well. I will give back the
camels and go back to my goat well!"

Farmyard Muddle

What a noise!
What muddle!
Can you sort it out?

The norse is heighing.

The grig is punting.

The mat is ceowing.

The beep is shaaing.

The squicken is chawking.

The mow is cooing.

And the bogs are darking.

Letters That Go Together

ck back, kicked, tricked

wh what, wheat, where

Sounds I Know

-ea beans **-oa** goat

-ee sheep **-ou** sprout

Words That Go Together

barnyard   farmyard

eggshells   scarecrow

Words I Know

about	back	know	said
after	farm	look	what
around	grow	plant	where
away	help	raise	world